DINOSAURS

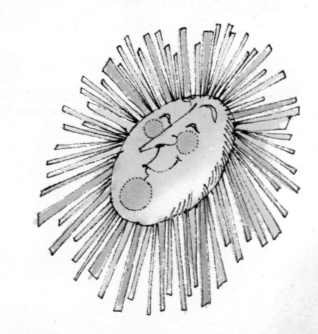

WILLIAM K. DURR · JEAN M. LE PERE · MARY LOU ALSIN

CONSULTANT · **PAUL McKEE**

LINGUISTIC ADVISOR · **JACK E. KITTELL**

HOUGHTON MIFFLIN COMPANY · BOSTON

ATLANTA · DALLAS · GENEVA, ILLINOIS · HOPEWELL, NEW JERSEY · PALO ALTO

Illustrated by **BILL MORRISON**

The BIGGEST One in the Play

PAM: Can you come to a play, Mother?
I'm going to be in it.

MOTHER: What a nice surprise!
Yes, I'll be there.

MOTHER: What will you be in the play?

PAM: It's a surprise.

I can't tell you now.

You'll see me.

I'm the biggest one in the play.

MOTHER: How can you be the biggest one?

You don't look big to me.

PAM: In this play I'm the biggest one.

PAM: Dad, can you come to a school play?
I'm going to be in it.

DAD: I can't come.
I have to work.

BILLY: Can I come?
I don't have to work.
And I like plays.

PAM: Yes, you can come.

DAD: What will you be in the play, Pam?

BILLY: Will you be a frog?

PAM: No, I will not be a frog.

I will not jump like a frog.

But I'll tell you this.

I'll be green like a frog.

And I'll be the biggest one in the play.

Look for the Biggest One

PAM: Will you come to my play, Mrs. Park?

MRS. PARK: Yes, I like plays.

Are you going to be a lion?

PAM: No, I will not be a lion.

I will not have teeth like a lion.

But I'll tell you this.

I'll help a lion to hide.

And I'll be the biggest one in the play.

BILLY: Where is she?

Where's Pam?

I can't see Pam.

MOTHER: Look for the biggest one.

That will be Pam.

BILLY: There she is!

She is green like a frog!

MRS. PARK: And she is helping a lion to hide.

MOTHER: Pam's a tree!

She's a big apple tree!

She is the biggest one in the play!

1. Did you find the biggest **needle?**

2. I don't like to play in the **grass.**

3. Is Sally hiding in the **barn?**

4. My mother will take me to **church.**

5. Do you have the **wheel** with you?

KEN: Walking little dogs is fun.

And it's not much work.

TED: But we don't get much for doing it.

How can we get to Fun Park this way?

After this I want to walk big dogs.

KEN: There's a big dog.

He's the biggest dog I've seen.

TED: Can we walk your nice big dog?

MR. GREEN: Yes, you can walk Chester.

But I'll tell you now.

He isn't much of a walker.

He likes to run.

TED: How can Chester run?

He can't see much, can he?

MR. GREEN: He can see where he's going.

It's no problem for Chester to run.

Chester's biggest problem is walking.

TED: He'll walk for me.

KEN: He's running away!

Look at that dog go!

You'll have to stop him.

What a Dog!

TED: Stop, Chester! Stop!

KEN: Now we do have a problem.

Look where he is.

And here comes a bus!

Oh! I'm scared to look at him!

TED: You can look now.

The bus is stopping.

POLICEMAN: Come and get your dog.

TED: He's not my dog.

This is Chester.

Get up, Chester! Get up!

You have to get up!

MAN: Take this hot dog.

A hot dog will get him up.

TED: Come here, Chester.

Come and get the hot dog.

KEN: He's getting up.

He wants it!

KEN: Oh, no! He's going into the library!

He can't take a hot dog in there!

TED: What a dog!

Dogs in the Library?

KEN: Chester! Chester!

MRS. WAY: Sh! Sh! Chester isn't in here.

There are no boys in the library.

Now take your dogs out.

TED: Chester's not a boy.

He's a dog.

And we have to take him for a walk.

TED: I see Chester!

MRS. WAY: You'll have to take him out!

KEN: He will not get up.
How can we take him out?

TED: I'll go and get help.

TED: Chester's in the library.

MR. GREEN: You walk dogs in the library?

TED: No. But Chester's in there.
And now we can't get him out.

MR. GREEN: We'll get Chester out of the library.

TED: No more big dogs for me!

KEN: Walking big dogs isn't much help.

TED: We'll have to walk more little dogs.
That's the way we'll get to Fun Park.

25

1. Where did you get your **tickets?**

2. Bill is looking at the **presents.**

3. It's hot. The boys are in the **shade.**

4. Now we will walk up the **steps.**

One-Way Tickets

PAM: I want to go in that lion.

I want to go and see the real lions.

DAD: You can't go without me.

And I have to wait here for Mother.

KEN: Ted and I will go.

Pam can go with us.

We can look after Pam.

DAD: I'll get tickets for the Jungle Bus.

KEN: You don't have to get tickets for us.
We walked dogs.

PAM: You can get my ticket, Dad.
I didn't walk dogs.

DAD: I'll wait here for you.

TED: The bus is stopping in the trees.

We are in the jungle now.

PAM: There are animal noises here.

KEN: There are candy apples in this jungle.

I can get candy apples for us.

PAM: I like this jungle more and more.

TED: Look at the tiger, Ken.

PAM: I want to play with a little lion.

KEN: You can't play with the lion, Pam.
And he can't have your candy apple.
He'll get sick.
The mother lion will not like that.

TED: Now Pam wants to play with a tiger.

Pam! You'll have to come with us.

We want to see more animals.

No Way Back

TED: We have to go back now.

There's a bus we can take.

MAN: Do you have tickets?

KEN: No, we don't have tickets.

MAN: You can get tickets there.

TED: Now we have a problem.

How will we get back without tickets?

PAM: Dad will come and get us.

KEN: No, Pam.

Dad's waiting for us.

PAM: I'll tell you what we can do.

KEN: You are little, Pam.

How can you know what to do?

PAM: I do know what we can do.

Look! Do you see the bus up there?

We can walk back the way it is going.

KEN: We can't wait here.

TED: The bus is going back that way.

PAM: I know it will work.

Come with me and you'll find out.

PAM: Here we are.

DAD: We have waited and waited for you.
How did you get here?

MOTHER: You didn't come back on a bus.

TED: The bus tickets are one-way tickets.

KEN: We walked back.

MOTHER: How did you know the way back?

KEN: We walked the way the bus comes.

DAD: You are lucky, Pam.
The boys did look after you.

PAM: Oh, no, Dad!
I looked after the boys.
Ted and Ken are the lucky ones!

The Treasure Hunt

KEN: This is a nice hot day for fishing.

Come to the park with me.

MIKE: We can't fish now, Ken.

We're going to have a treasure hunt.

KEN: I'll hunt for treasure with you.

And I know I'll win.

MIKE: You can't play, Ken.

You have to know how to read.

And you don't want to read.

KEN: Reading is work, and I don't like it.

But treasure hunts are fun.

I can be in the treasure hunt.

PATTY: How can you win, Ken?

You have to read the cards.

The cards tell you what to find.

KEN: I can read a little.

I'll find the treasures.

And I'll win this treasure hunt!

PATTY: The hunt is on now.

Get going.

I'll wait here for all of you.

Walk to the park.
Go to the ～～～.
Look for a big tree.
Find a box there.

KEN: There's a picture on this card.

The picture tells me what to get.

I don't have to know how to read.

43

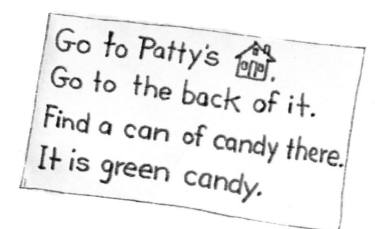

Go to Patty's 🏠.
Go to the back of it.
Find a can of candy there.
It is green candy.

KEN: This treasure hunt is funny.
How can I get a house?

PAM: What's that for?

KEN: It's for a treasure hunt.
The cards tell me what to get.

Funny Treasures

KEN: Now I have to get a house. See?

PAM: Oh! It looks like my playhouse.

KEN: This is my lucky day!
Can I take your playhouse?
You'll get it back.

PAM: Is that all you have to get?

KEN: No! I have to get more treasures.
But I know I'll win.

DAD: Where are you going with all that?

KEN: I'm on my way to get more treasures.
I'm winning a treasure hunt.

DAD: What a funny treasure hunt!
How did you know what to get?

KEN: I looked at the cards.

DAD: Can I see one of the cards?

DAD: Did you read this card, Ken?

KEN: I looked at the picture of the house.

DAD: But you're to get a can of candy.

KEN: Oh, I didn't know that, Dad.
I can't read the cards.

DAD: I'll help you with reading.
Winning treasure hunts is fun.
And **reading** will help you to win.

PATTY: Where are your treasures, Ken?

KEN: I didn't find the treasures.

The pictures didn't help me much.

But Dad will help me with my reading.

Then I'll win a treasure hunt.

1. Can you help me with this **knot?**

2. I don't know where the **fins** are.

3. Come with us on the **sailboat.**

4. Look for the treasure in a big **chest.**

5. Then Mother will get the **towel.**

RED IS NICE

MIKE: Do you want to go to the library, Ken?

KEN: I can't go with you now.

I have to paint this tree house red.

MIKE: I'm good at painting tree houses.

I can help you paint it.

Then we can go to the library.

MIKE: **That looks good!**

Red is a good color for a tree house.

KEN: **We got paint on the doghouse!**

53

KEN: I know what we can do.

Dad got all this red paint for me.

And red's a good color for a doghouse.

We'll paint the doghouse red.

MIKE: I'm getting sick of painting!

KEN: We can't stop now.

KEN: There! The doghouse is painted.

MIKE: We got red paint on the fence!
Do we have much more paint?

KEN: Yes. We'll have to paint the fence.

MIKE: Red is a good color for a fence.
We'll paint the fence.
Then we can go to the library.

More Painting?

KEN: This will surprise Dad!

MIKE: I'm hot, and I'm sick of painting.
Can't we go to the library now?

KEN: No. We have to get this painted.
Get to work.

KEN: There! The fence is red.

MIKE: Will your dad like it?

KEN: We'll find out.
Here he comes now.

DAD: What's going on here, boys?

KEN: I had to paint my tree house.
And paint got on the doghouse.

MIKE: Then we had to paint the doghouse.

KEN: And paint got on the fence.
Then we had to paint the fence.

MIKE: Oh, Ken! We got paint on the house!

KEN: We'll have to paint the house.
Red's a good color for a house.

DAD: Look, boys!
There's red paint on you!
We'll have to paint you.

KEN: Oh, no! Red isn't a good color for me.

MIKE: I don't want to be painted red.

DAD: And I don't want a red house!

1. Billy is a good **reader.**

2. Is Jan the **winner?**

3. Pam is helping the **painter.**

4. The biggest **player** is Ken.

5. You are a good **jumper,** Sally.

6. The **waiter** is Mr. Day.

The Animal With No Name

MRS. HUNT: Your mothers will be here.

We've got more work to do.

PATTY: I painted this picture.

It's a green tree with red apples.

MRS. HUNT: That painting is nice, Patty.

Put your name on it.

Then make a book for your work.

MIKE: I'll make something with this.

I can make a little tiger.

MRS. HUNT: What did you make, Ted?

I don't see it here.

TED: I can't make things.

I'm going to read a book.

MRS. HUNT: Ted, you can make something.

Look at all the things here.

You can find something to work with.

TED: I can't do it.

The things I make look funny.

MRS. HUNT: You can help us, Ted.

You can put things away.

TED: I know I can do that!

MIKE: Look at my little tiger.

I put a big smile on him.

What will I do with this can of paint?

TED: I'll take it.

KEN: My lion is the biggest animal of all.

Its teeth can scare tigers.

Where can I put this box?

TED: I know what to do with it!

A Funny Animal

PATTY: Here's some paint to put away, Ted.

TED: Put it there, Patty.

I know what to do with it.

MRS. HUNT: Here are more animals.

Your work looks nice.

I know your mothers will like it.

PATTY: What's Ted doing?

MRS. HUNT: He's helping to put things away.

MIKE: No, he's working on something.

MRS. HUNT: Oh, Ted! What did you make?

TED: It's a big animal with funny colors.

It's not a jungle animal.

And it's not in picture books.

MIKE: What name will you put on the card?

TED: That's no problem.

I have a name for my animal.

TED: I'm lucky!

I did make something good.

This animal will be a surprise.

I can't wait for my mother to see it.

1. We are going to paint the fence.

   We don't want a red fence.

   What color will we paint it?

2. Patty is helping mother.

   They are making something good.

   What will it be?

3. Billy is looking for a rocket.

   Billy's mother put it away.

   Where will he find it?

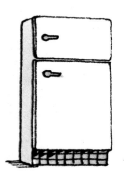

FOOTPRINTS

MIKE: What are you doing with that?

PATTY: I'm finding footprints, Mike.
Then I look in this book.
Here's a cat's footprint.

MIKE: I know that's a cat's footprint.
And I don't have a book.

PATTY: You don't know all the footprints.
Take a look at this book.

MIKE: Look at this footprint, Patty.

It's the biggest one in the book.

And a dinosaur makes it.

PATTY: But there are no more dinosaurs now.

We can't look for that footprint!

MIKE: Here's a funny footprint.
Find this one in your book.

PATTY: It's not in the book.

MIKE: Something had to make this footprint.
And it's something in your house.

PATTY: Oh, Mike! It's my mother!
She makes funny footprints.

PATTY: Hunting for footprints is fun!

MIKE: Patty! Look at this big footprint!
It's like that big one in your book.

PATTY: There are no dinosaurs now.
That can't be a dinosaur footprint.

MIKE: But it's like the one in the book.
It's got to be a dinosaur footprint.

PATTY: The footprints go this way.

I'm going after that dinosaur.

MIKE: I don't want a dinosaur to get me.

I'm scared to hunt dinosaurs.

PATTY: The dinosaur will not get us.

We'll hide here.

We can look out and see it.

But the dinosaur will not see us.

MIKE: I can't see the dinosaur.

We'll have to run to that tree.

A Dinosaur in the Tree House?

PATTY: The dinosaur is going to Ken's house!

MIKE: The footprints stop at the tree.

Sh! Don't make a noise.

The dinosaur is in Ken's tree house.

It's waiting to jump out at us.

We'll have to tell Ken.

MIKE: Ken, do you know what?

KEN: No, what?

MIKE: A dinosaur is up in your tree house.

PATTY: Look at this dinosaur footprint.
It's like a footprint in my book.

KEN: I know where that dinosaur is.
Wait here.
I'll be back.

PATTY: We're good at finding footprints.

A cat's footprints!

My mother's footprints!

And Ken's footprints!

CDEFGHIJ·B·7821098765 4